SPRING POPS UP

Written by Meish Goldish
Illustrated by Obadinah Heavner

HARCOURT BRACE & COMPANY

Orlando   Atlanta   Austin   Boston   San Francisco   Chicago   Dallas   New York
Toronto   London

A stem pops up.

A leaf pops up.

A flower pops up.

A garden pops up.

A worm pops up.

A bug pops up.

Lunch time!